# JULES VERNE'S
# JOURNEY TO THE CENTRE OF THE EARTH

## RETOLD BY DAVIS WORTH MILLER
## AND KATHERINE MCLEAN BREVARD
## ILLUSTRATED BY GREG REBIS
## COLOUR BY PROTOBUNKER STUDIO

Librarian Reviewer
Katharine Kan
Graphic novel reviewer and Library Consultant

Reading Consultant
Elizabeth Stedem
Educator and Consultant

Raintree

**www.raintreepublishers.co.uk**
Visit our website to find out
more information about
Raintree books.

**To order:**
☎ Phone 0845 6044371
🖷 Fax +44 (0) 1865 312263
🖳 Email myorders@raintreepublishers.co.uk

Customers from outside the UK please telephone +44 1865 312262

Raintree is an imprint of Capstone Global Library Limited, a company incorporated
in England and Wales having its registered office at 7 Pilgrim Street, London, EC4V 6LB –
Registered company number: 6695582

Text © Stone Arch Books 2008
First published in the United Kingdom in hardback and paperback by
Capstone Global Library Limited in 2011
The moral rights of the proprietor have been asserted.

Art Director: Heather Kindseth
Graphic Designer: Kay Fraser
Editor: Laura Knowles
Originated by Capstone Global Library Ltd
Printed and bound in China by Leo Paper Products Ltd

ISBN 978 1 406 22494 8 (hardback)
15 14 13 12 11
10 9 8 7 6 5 4 3 2 1

ISBN 978 1 406 22500 6 (paperback)
15 14 13 12 11
10 9 8 7 6 5 4 3 2 1

**British Library Cataloguing in Publication Data**
A full catalogue record for this book is available from the British Library.

# CONTENTS

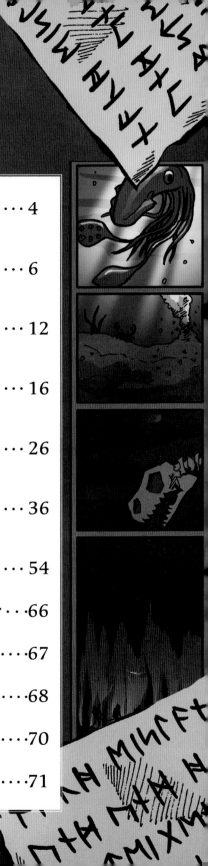

INTRODUCING . . .

Arne Saknussemm

Otto Lidenbrock

Hans Bjelke

Axel Lidenbrock

Hamburg, Germany, May 1862

Axel, follow me. I've made the most remarkable discovery.

Look what I found in an old bookshop.

This 300-year-old book belonged to the famous Icelandic explorer, Arne Saknussemm.

Then perhaps you shouldn't lose this, Uncle.

The paper consisted of mysterious handwritten characters.

Uncle Lidenbrock and I tried not only Runic but many other languages. We worked until exhaustion overtook us.

Blast! We'll never discover the meaning of these words!

Uncle stormed out of the house.

My own exhaustion, along with the heat, was nearly too much for me. Fanning myself with the paper, I saw it from behind.

Through the back I read the Latin words **craterem** and **terrestre** - crater and earth. I found the secret! All it took to decode the message was to read it backwards!

When my uncle returned, I told him the secret.

Backwards! Of course!

He quickly translated the document.

Go to Iceland and descend into the crater of Sneffels. A long shadow of the mountain will point to the right spot at the end of June. If you do this, bold traveller, you will reach the centre of the earth. I know. I have done it.

—Arne Saknussemm

# CHAPTER ② OUR JOURNEY BEGINS

We travelled by ship. The ten-day trip was hard. The seas were rough and wild.

When we finally reached Iceland, my seasick uncle stepped out on deck, and his face brightened with a smile.

Behold! Mount Sneffels! The gateway to the centre of the earth.

The next morning, I awoke to my uncle speaking Danish from the next room at the inn. I joined him and was introduced to a large man.

Axel, my boy, meet Hans Bjelke. Hans will be our guide.

Monday, 29th June 1862. At the top of the mountain, I stared down into a gigantic volcanic crater.

This is insanity! Going down there is like climbing into a cannon that's ready to explode.

Where science has led us, we must follow.

We began our descent, passing volcanic rocks and deep, soft snow.

After a few hours we reached the bottom of the crater, where we found three black pits. When Sneffels last erupted in 1229, these pits had spat out lava and poisonous gases.

Axel, come here. How wonderful!

There, carved on the rock wall, was the name I'd hoped never to see again: Arne Saknussemm.

At noon exactly, the shadow of Mount Sneffels pointed towards the central pit.

Forward, my friends. Forward to the greatest adventure of all. Forward to the centre of the earth!

The next day, our real journey began. We stepped to the mouth of the central pit. The sides dropped straight down and ended in nothingness. I became dizzy.

My legs went weak.

If not for Hans, I would have fallen to my death.

With a rope tied around a lump of hardened lava, we began our descent.

That night . . .

Less than 48 hours into our expedition and we only have enough water for five more days. Doesn't this concern you, Uncle?

No reason to worry. We'll find plenty of water along the way.

On Wednesday, 1st July, at six o'clock in the morning, we continued on.

During those several days, we still did not find water. We began to ration what was left in our pouches.

Saturday, 4th July.

A dead end! We're not on the path taken by Arne Saknussemm. Let's sleep tonight. Tomorrow we'll go back to where this tunnel began.

That journey will take three days, Uncle. Our water's almost gone.

And your courage with it?

**Sunday, 5th July.** Our water gave out completely on the next day's march.

**Tuesday, 7th July.** Without water for three days, we arrived half-dead back at the beginning of the two tunnels.

I fell unconscious . . .

We must go back to Sneffels, Uncle.

23

Wednesday, 8th July. We began our second descent. This new tunnel had types of rocks never seen by any scientist.

As we stepped into a chamber of clear white mica, the beams from our lamps were reflected all around us.

It looks like we are inside a giant diamond!

Soon, however, my legs began to fail me. Suddenly I couldn't see.

Help, help, I'm dying.

**Thursday, 9th July.**
The next morning, we ate breakfast and drank cool water from the murmuring stream. The harshness of the past week's journey was forgotten.

The tunnel moved sharply downwards. It twisted and turned. On Friday evening, we figured our position to be 90 miles southeast of Sneffels and 8 miles deep.

We were in for a startling surprise.

Now we shall make real progress!

A frightening abyss opened at our feet. My uncle clapped his hands with joy when he saw how steep it was.

The rocks almost form a staircase.

We should be able to make our way down.

We followed the staircase deeper and deeper into the earth, the loyal stream flowing beside us.

Our spiral road carried us 20 miles below sea level.

Our toil took us deeper into the earth. Above our heads: rocks, ocean, a continent, entire cities of people.

Over the next two weeks, the slopes became more dangerous. Some were almost vertical, and we had to descend with ropes.

29

Half an hour later, there was still no response. Only my voice echoing off those terrible rock walls.

No reason to panic. I had the stream to guide me to my uncle and Hans.

I stooped to plunge my hands into the faithful water . . .

The stream has disappeared!

33

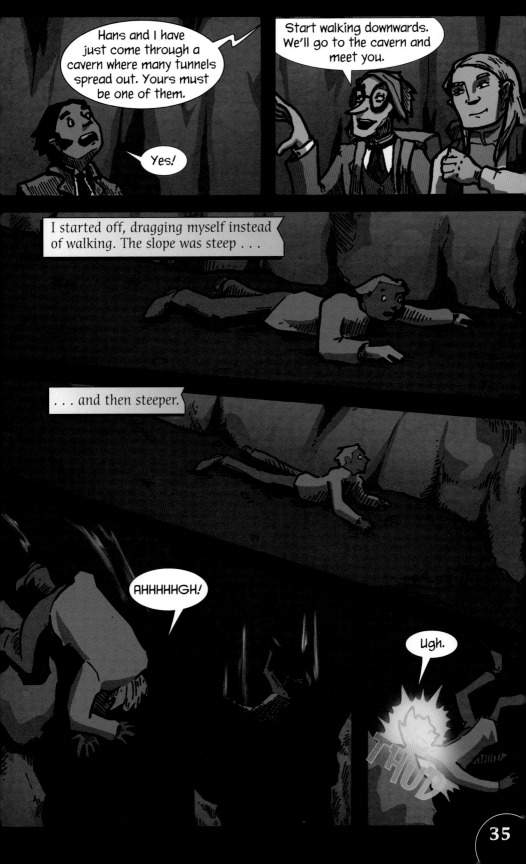

35

# CHAPTER **5** THE GREAT SEA

I was dreaming of the ocean and the waves hitting the beach. Then, I awoke.

Where am I?

My uncle came running.

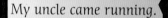

He's alive! Axel's alive!

You fell down a tunnel into Hans's arms.

Hans treated your wounds with a special Icelandic ointment.

After we'd walked about a mile, a dense forest appeared in the distance. Trees shaped like umbrellas stood motionless, despite the strong breeze.

As we made it to their shade, I found myself in a forest of giant mushrooms!

We walked on and saw wonders with every step.

These ferns are larger than our trees back home!

41

**Tuesday, 18th August.** That evening, two hours after I fell asleep, I was awoken by a massive bump.

Hans pointed to a huge shape rolling in and out of the waves less than a mile away.

A colossal porpoise!

A sea lizard!

Those teeth are as long as daggers!

On the other side of the raft were a sea turtle and a serpent, both of them giants!

I picked up my rifle, but Hans stopped me. What effect could a bullet have on these monsters?

The serpent came near on the left side of the raft, the sea lizard on the right. The other creatures had disappeared.

The eye of the ichthyosaurus was as large as my head!

Soon, the creatures fell into a hissing, screeching battle!

The monsters disappeared beneath the surface, nearly pulling us into the whirlpool they left behind.

Minutes passed, and then an enormous head shot up out of the water.

The plesiosaurus has been killed!

When the ichthyosaurus did not reappear, we set sail and travelled more than 800 miles - putting us directly under England!

Fate is having fun with me, is it? Well, I won't give in.

Uncle, we can't fight that sea again. It almost killed us!

To the raft!

Hans loaded our supplies.

We won't start until tomorrow. We're far east of Port Gretchen, and I won't leave this part of the coast until I've explored it.

My uncle and I followed the shores of the Lidenbrock Sea until we came upon great mounds of bones stretching away to the horizon.

Leaving the forest, we quickly arrived back at the shore of the Lidenbrock Sea. We found two huge rocks and the entrance to a dark tunnel.

Arne Saknussemm!

He was here!

For once, I was happy to hear the ancient explorer's name.

Let's follow his trail!

Let's go back to Hans and sail the raft to this spot.

That evening we returned to the cave. My uncle had his lantern.
We'd gone a dozen yards when we were stopped by a big boulder.

At some point since Saknussemm's journey, this boulder closed off the passage.

We could use the gunpowder to blow it up.

We dug a hole big enough to hold our entire stock of gunpowder. Then we trailed a long fuse to a point outside the cave.

May I light the fuse?

Of course, my boy. Then we'll wait safely out at sea.

We should be out of danger here.

We're going up!

We were, indeed, heading up, at an amazing speed!

The temperature was quickly rising.

If we're not drowned or smashed to pieces, we'll be burned alive!

Where there's life, there's hope.

We were in Sicily, at the edge of the Mediterranean Sea. We'd entered the earth by one volcano and come out by another, over 3,000 miles apart.

Four months after first discovering the map, we returned home. While we were gone, news of our journey had spread throughout Hamburg and around the world.

Now that you're a hero, Axel, you'll never need to leave me again.

The next day Hans left for Iceland. I'll always remember the brave guide who shared our adventures and saved our lives. He made my uncle the happiest of scientists, and me the happiest of men.

And I would always remember my amazing journey to the centre of the earth!

# ABOUT JULES VERNE

Jules Verne was born in France on 8th February 1828. Growing up near a river, the constant sight of ships sparked his interest in travel. As a young man, Verne even tried to run away and become a cabin boy. Fortunately, his father caught him, and soon Verne was off to study law in Paris. While there, Verne escaped the boredom of his studies by writing stories. When his father found out about this hobby, he stopped sending money for school. Verne started selling his stories, many of which became popular, including *Journey to the Centre of the Earth* in 1864. Before he died in 1905, the author bought a boat and sailed around Europe.

# ABOUT THE RETELLING AUTHORS

Davis Worth Miller and Katherine McLean Brevard are a married couple who work together. They are both full-time writers. Miller has written several best-selling books. He is now working on a memoir and on several novels with his wife.

# ABOUT THE ILLUSTRATOR

After working in civic government, pizza delivery, music retail, and proofreading, Greg Rebis eventually landed work in publishing, film, and graphics. Greg still loves art, sci-fi, and video games.

# GLOSSARY

**abyss** very, very deep pit

**ancient** existing a long time ago

**expedition** long journey taken for a specific purpose

**ichthyosaurus** large, extinct reptile that looked a bit like a dolphin with a toothed snout, which lived about 250 million years ago

**mastodon** extinct mammal that looked like a gigantic elephant

**plesiosaurus** large, extinct ocean reptile with a small head, short tail, and turtle-like body

**prehistoric** happening in a time before history was written down

**ration** use only a small amount

**specimen** small sample to be used in scientific tests

# MORE ABOUT EARTH'S CENTRE

The author, Jules Verne, imagined Earth's interior was filled with rivers, oceans, dinosaurs, and giant mushrooms. Scientists, however, believe the centre of our planet is made up of even more amazing things!

Think of Earth as an egg. An egg has three parts: the shell, the egg white, and the yolk. Earth also has three main layers: the crust, the mantle, and the core.

## The crust

Just like the shell of an egg, the crust is the hard, outer layer of Earth. It is also the thinnest layer. Beneath the oceans, the crust is only about 10 kilometres thick. The crust is made up mostly of rocks, such as granite and basalt.

## The mantle

Underneath the crust is the thickest layer. At about 2,900 kilometres thick, the mantle makes up nearly 80 per cent of Earth. This layer is extremely hot as well. So hot, in fact, that much of the rocky material has melted into liquid!

## The core

Earth's core has two parts: the outer core and the inner core. Both sections contain iron and nickel. In the outer core, these elements melt into liquid as temperatures approach 4,700 degrees Celsius. Despite being an even hotter temperature, the inner core remains solid under extreme pressure. This solid ball is about the size of the Moon!

Scientists use high-tech equipment to make predictions about Earth's centre, but they've never actually been there. In fact, the deepest hole ever drilled is only about 12 kilometres into the crust. The centre of Earth is more than 6,000 kilometres beneath our feet! If we think of Earth as an egg, our deepest hole would just scratch the egg's shell.

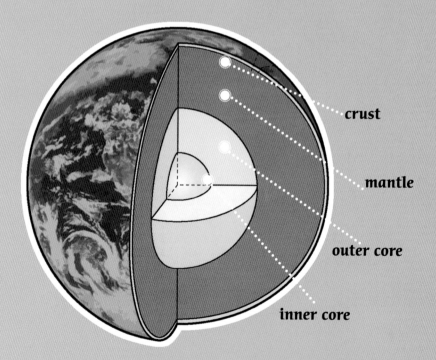

crust

mantle

outer core

inner core

# DISCUSSION QUESTIONS

**1.** Each of the explorers had different skills that helped the group survive the journey. Name at least one skill for each character. Who do you think was most important to the group's survival? Why?

**2.** Axel, Uncle Lidenbrock, and Hans nearly ran out of water. Instead of returning to the surface, they took a risk and continued their journey. Are all risks good? Think of an example of a good risk and a bad risk.

**3.** At the end of the story, we find out that Axel and Uncle Lidenbrock never returned to the centre of the earth. Why do you think they never went back? Would you have gone back? Explain your answer.

# WRITING PROMPTS

**1.** The explorers in the story bought many supplies for their journey. Still, they almost did not survive. If you were taking the same journey and could only bring three things, what would they be? Explain your choices.

**2.** Find a globe or a map of the world. With your eyes closed, point to a place on the globe or map. Wherever your finger lands, write an adventure story about how you would travel there and what you would find.

**3.** Sometimes authors can't think of an idea for a story. If you ever have this problem, try starting with a title. Write a story with the title *Journey to the Centre of the Moon*. How will your characters get to the Moon? What will they find there?

# GRAPHIC REVOLVE

If you have enjoyed this story, there are many more exciting tales for you to discover in the Graphic Revolve collection...

20,000 Leagues Under the Sea
The Adventures of Tom Sawyer
Alice in Wonderland
Black Beauty
Dracula
Frankenstein
Gulliver's Travels
The Hound of the Baskervilles
The Hunchback of Notre Dame
Journey to the Centre of the Earth
The Jungle Book
King Arthur and the Knights of the Round Table
The Legend of Sleepy Hollow
Robin Hood
The Strange Case of Dr Jeckyll and Mr Hyde
The Swiss Family Robinson
Treasure Island
The Wizard of Oz